Dora Helps Save The Earth!

by Emily Sollinger   illustrated by Dave Aikins

SIMON AND SCHUSTER/NICKELODEON

Based on the TV series *Dora the Explorer* as seen on Nickelodeon

SIMON AND SCHUSTER
First published in Great Britain in 2009 by Simon & Schuster UK Ltd
1st Floor, 222 Gray's Inn Road, London WC1X 8HB
A CBS Company

Originally published in the USA in 2009 by Simon Spotlight,
an imprint of Simon & Schuster Children's Division, New York.

A CIP catalogue record for this book is available from the British Library

Printed on Satimat Green and Oxygen 50:50, both papers comprising 50% recovered fibre
and 50% virgin fibre certified by The Forest Stewardship Council.

Printed by Pureprint Group using **pureprint**® environmental print technology. All production systems are certified to ISO
14001:2004 and registered to EMAS environmental management systems. The printing inks are made from vegetable based oils and
no harmful isopropyl alcohol was used in the printing process. All the electricity was generated from renewable sources and on
average 94% of any dry waste associated with this production will be recycled.
Pureprint Group holds The Queen's Award for Enterprise: Sustainable Development and is a CarbonNeutral® company, all CO_2
emissions associated with the production of this publication have been reduced to net zero.

CERTIFIED
CARBON
NEUTRAL®
publication
CarbonNeutral.com
CO₂ emissions reduced to
net zero in accordance with
The CarbonNeutral Protocol

THE QUEEN'S AWARDS
FOR ENTERPRISE:
SUSTAINABLE DEVELOPMENT
2008

ISBN: 978-1-84738-493-5

Printed in Great Britain

10 9 8 7 6 5 4 3 2 1

Visit our websites: www.simonsays.co.uk
www.nickjr.co.uk

¡Hola! I'm Dora! Today we're having a party at Play Park to celebrate the Earth. We will learn about ways to take care of the Earth. There are lots of things we can do every day to help protect it.

I have an idea! I'm going to ask all of my friends and family what they do to help save the Earth. I'll put all of their tips in a scrapbook that I can take to the party to share with everyone.

My best friend, Boots, says he always makes sure not to waste water. He takes short showers and turns off the tap when he's brushing his teeth. Can you think of any other ways to save water?

Here's a recycling idea! If you have water left in your drinking glass, you can use it to water your house plants. Do you see any plants that need watering?

WAYS TO SAVE WATER!

1. _____

2. _____

3. _____

My *mami* says it's important to turn off the lights when we aren't using them. We can save a lot of energy this way. We can also turn out the lights during the day when there is plenty of sunlight. How else can we save energy?

My cousin Diego knows a great way to save energy. He always rides his bike to school instead of riding in a car. You can also walk, roller-skate, skip, or run! Diego says these are great ways to spend time outdoors and get exercise while keeping the air clean. Sometimes he even finds animals to rescue along the way!

My Bike

SAVE ENERGY

My *papi* loves to cook. When he goes to the supermarket to buy groceries, he brings his own cloth bags with him. He reuses the same bags every time he goes shopping.

REUSE

Reuse!

When *Papi* makes my lunch, he puts it in a special bag. We wash the bag, and I can use it again!

My *abuela* is careful about saving energy too. When she's cooking or preparing food, she always decides what she wants to get before opening the refrigerator door. If you leave the door open for a long time, you'll let out cold air and the refrigerator will use more energy to keep working.

Even my baby brother and sister can help save the Earth. When the twins outgrow their toys and books, we won't throw them away. Instead, we'll pass them along to other babies who can use them.

DONATIONS

SHARE

My friend Isa loves to plant fruits, vegetables, trees, and flowers in her garden. Growing flowers, trees, and other plants helps make the air we breathe clean and fresh. It's a great thing to do to help save the Earth.

My friend Benny saves energy by playing outside whenever he can. There are so many games we can play outside. I love football! What's your favourite outdoor game?

LET'S PLAY!!!

Power Off!

SHUT DOWN!

My friend Tico always makes sure to recycle properly. He separates cans, bottles, and paper from the rubbish and places them in special containers. The cans, bottles, and paper can be recycled and used to make other things - like books and toys! I can see some things that need to be recycled. Can you see them? Where?

I'm so glad that all of my friends and family work so hard to help take care of the Earth. I learned a lot from them. Did you?

Now it's time to go to the party in Play Park. Oh, no! It looks like there's rubbish along the path. Will you help me pick it up?

Hooray! We cleared the path to the park. Thanks so much for helping. Now I'm going to share my recycling scrapbook with everyone at the party!

Let's help save the Earth every day!